Edition Schott

xophone

Bernhard Heiden
1910 – 2000

Sonata

for Alto Saxophone in E♭ and Piano
für Altsaxophon in Es und Klavier

ED 11195
ISMN 979-0-2201-0871-6

www.schott-music.com

Mainz · London · Berlin · Madrid · New York · Paris · Prague · Tokyo · Toronto
© 1943 SCHOTT MUSIC Ltd, London · Printed in Germany

SONATA
for
Saxophone and Piano

BERNHARD HEIDEN (1937)

I

4

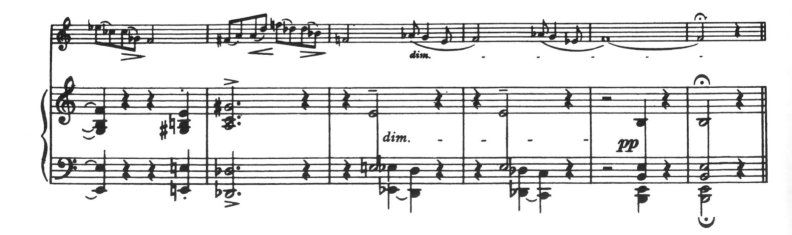

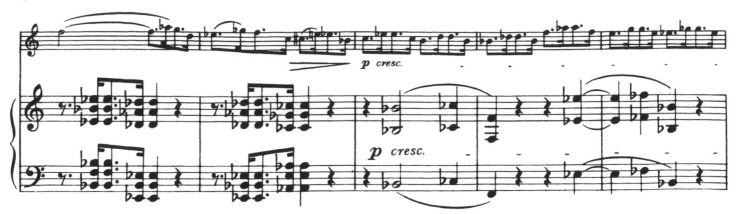

II

②

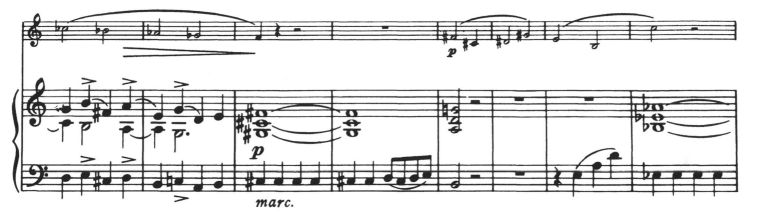

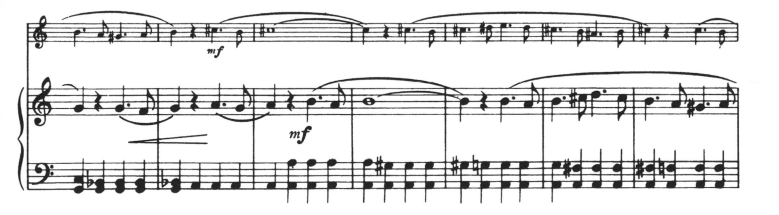

III

Presto

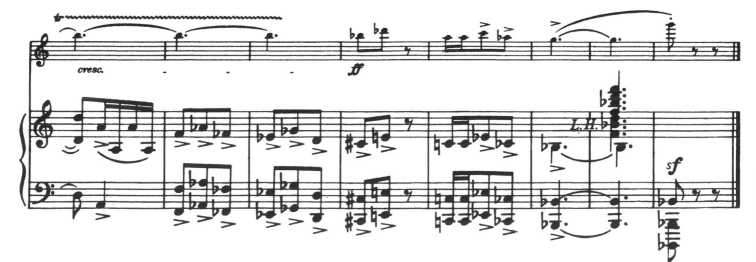

Detroit, Mich.

Schott Music Ltd, London S&Co.6395